My Family

written by Karen Hjemboe
illustrated by Dorothy Sullivan

Bebop Books

An imprint of LEE & LOW BOOKS Inc.

My mother teaches me.

My father teaches me.

My sister teaches me.

My brother teaches me.

My grandmother teaches me.

My grandfather teaches me.

My family teaches me.
Who teaches you?